Bolton
Council

Please return/renew this item
by the last date shown.
Books may also be renewed by
phone or the Internet.

JF Tonge

Tel: 01204 332384
www.bolton.gov.uk/libraries

www.raintreepublishers.co.uk
Visit our website to find out
more information about
Raintree books.

To order:
☎ Phone 0845 6044371
🖹 Fax +44 (0) 1865 312263
📧 Email myorders@raintreepublishers.co.uk

Customers from outside the UK please telephone +44 1865 312262

Raintree is an imprint of Capstone Global Library Limited,
a company incorporated in England and Wales having its registered
office at 7 Pilgrim Street, London, EC4V 6LB
– Registered company number: 6695582

First published by Stone Arch Books in 2010
First published in the United Kingdom in paperback in 2012
The moral rights of the proprietor have been asserted.

Edited by Laura Knowles
Originated by Capstone Global Library Ltd
Printed and bound in China by South China Printing Company

ISBN 978 1 406 23718 4 (paperback)
16 15 14 13 12
10 9 8 7 6 5 4 3 2 1

British Library Cataloguing in Publication Data
A full catalogue record for this book is available
from the British Library.

In a strange corner of the world known as Transylmania . . .

Legendary monsters were born.

WELCOME TO TRANSYLMANIA

But long before their frightful fame, these classic creatures faced fears of their own.

To take on terrifying teachers and homework horrors,
they formed the most fearsome friendship on Earth . . .

Mighty Mighty MONSTERS

Vlad

Talbot

Witchita

Milton

Poto

Frankie

Igor

Mary

Late one night, in the secret clubhouse of the Mighty Mighty Monsters . . .
Welcome, Monsters, to the weekly hide-and-seek competition!
TRANSYLMANIA TOWN HALL

As you know, we're here to set a few rules.
MIGHTY
MIGHTY

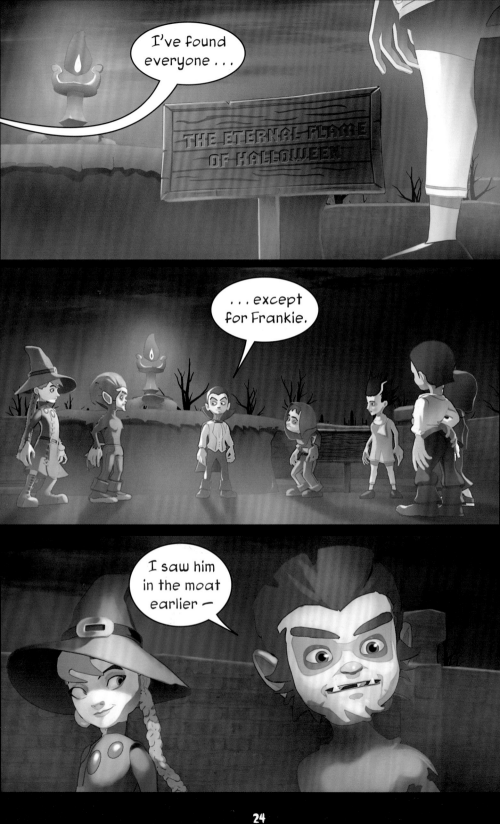

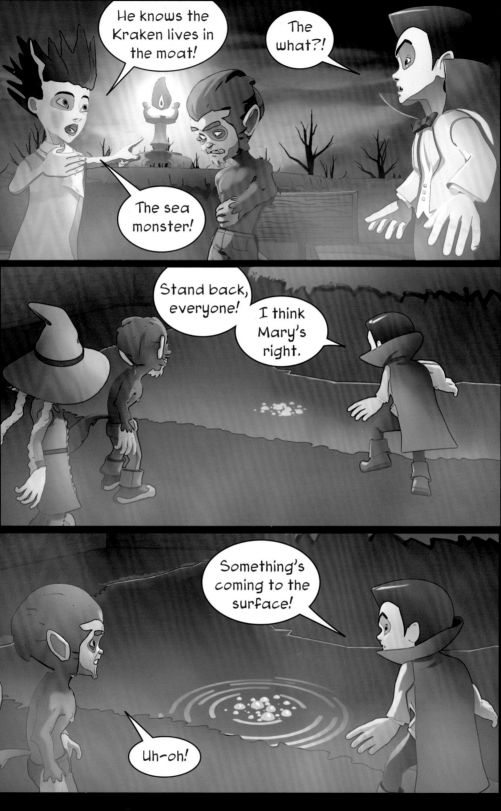

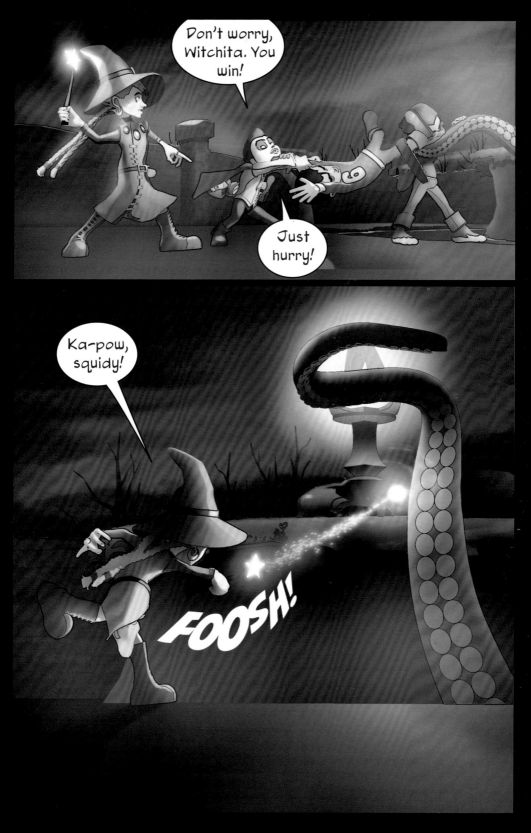

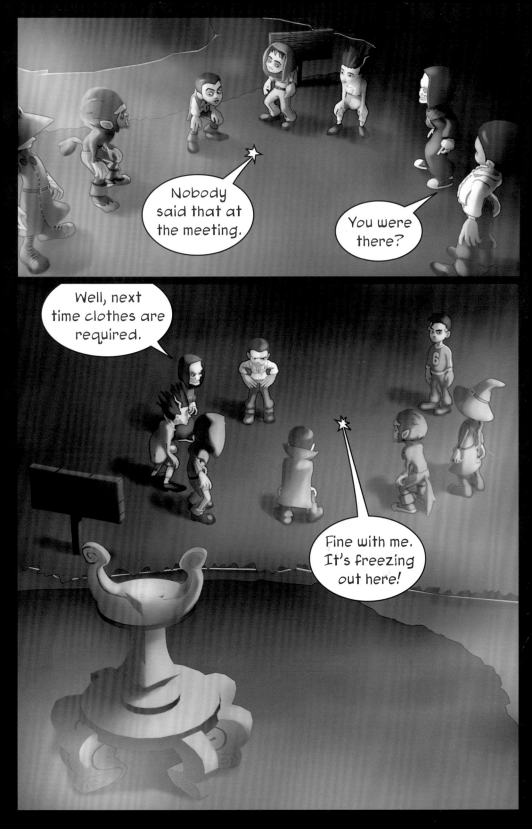

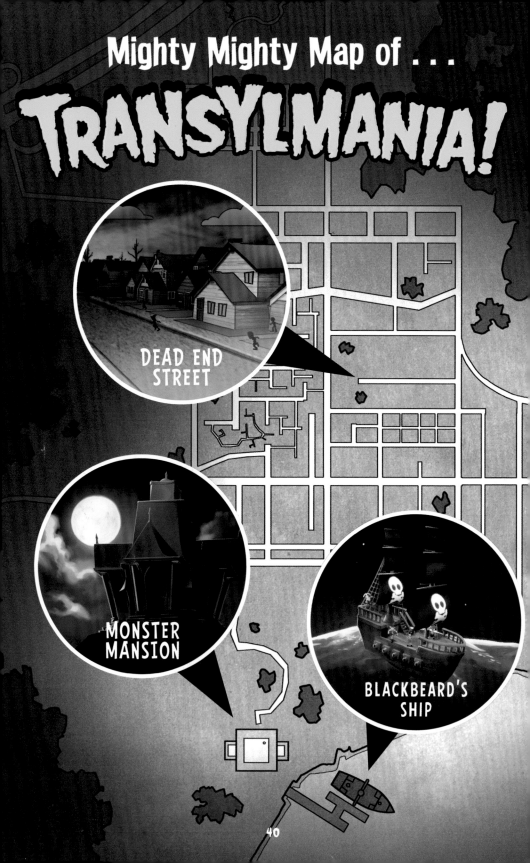

Mighty Mighty Map of . . .
TRANSYLMANIA!

DEAD END STREET

MONSTER MANSION

BLACKBEARD'S SHIP

SPOOKY
FOREST

MONSTER
SCHOOL

FLAME OF
HALLOWEEN

CASTLE OF
DOOM

Mighty Mighty MONSTERS

...BEFORE THEY WERE STARS!

VLAD

Nickname: The Count

Hometown: Transylmania

Favourite colour: blood red

Favourite animal: bats

Mighty mighty powers: the ability to live forever; the power of flight; able to transform into a bat; superpowered fangs.

BIOGRAPHY

Every team needs a leader, and Vlad is more than happy to fill that role for the Mighty Mighty Monsters. Although he's a picky eater (hates garlic, but loves blood!), Vlad never met a monster he didn't like. When a member of the Mighty Mighty Monsters is in trouble, he's always willing to lend a hand (or a wing). These days, Vlad is still one of the most famous monsters on Earth.

In 1897, author Bram Stoker published *Dracula*, the first book ever written about this blood-sucking monster.

Some believe the author based the novel on a real-life person known as Vlad Dracula. In the mid-1400s, this evil leader ruled over what is today Romania.

In 1931, actor Bela Lugosi starred in a film adaptation of the novel. Since then, many films featuring Count Dracula have been made, and vampire stories have become popular worldwide.

About Sean O'Reilly
and Arcana Studio

As a lifelong comics fan, Sean O'Reilly dreamed of becoming a comic book creator. In 2004, he realized that dream by creating Arcana Studio. In one short year, O'Reilly took his studio from a one-person operation in his house to an award-winning comic book publisher with more than 150 graphic novels produced for Harper Collins, Simon & Schuster, Random House, Scholastic, and others.

Within a year, the company won many awards including the Shuster Award for Outstanding Publisher and the Moonbeam Award for top children's graphic novel. O'Reilly also won the Top 40 Under 40 award from the city of Vancouver and authored *The Clockwork Girl* for Top Graphic Novel at Book Expo America in 2009.

Currently, O'Reilly is one of the most prolific independent comic book writers in Canada. While showing no signs of slowing down in comics, he now also writes screenplays and adapts his creations for the big screen.

GLOSSARY

clubhouse house used by a group or club

competition contest of some kind, such as a game of hide-and-seek

gavel small, wooden mallet often used to begin a meeting or to call for quiet

insurance protection against sickness, theft, accidents, or losses

Kraken sea monster

moat deep, wide ditch filled with water, which surrounds a building or area to protect it

mood the way a person feels

motion formal suggestion made at a meeting

Mozart famous composer of music who lived during the 1700s

provide supply the things that someone needs

required something that must be done

DISCUSSION QUESTIONS

1. What Mighty Mighty Monster do you think would be the most difficult to find in a game of hide-and-seek? Why?

2. Witchita had to break the rules of the game to save her friend. Do you think this decision was okay? Explain.

3. All of the Mighty Mighty Monsters are different. Which character do you like the best and why?

WRITING PROMPTS

1. In this story, the Mighty Mighty Monsters make up their own rules for hide-and-seek. Write down the rules for your very own game. Give it a name. Then see if others want to play!

2. If you could be any monster, which monster would you be? Write about your choice and the adventures you would have.

3. Write your own Mighty Mighty Monsters adventure. What will the ghoulish gang do next? What villains will they face? You decide.

FIND OUT MORE

INFORMATION BOOKS

The Mystery of Vampires and Werewolves (Can Science Solve?), Chris Oxlade (Heinemann Library, 2008)

Vampires and the Undead (Dark Side), Anita Ganeri (Wayland, 2010)

GRAPHIC NOVELS

Dracula (Graphic Revolve), Bram Stoker, retold by Michael Burgan (Raintree, 2009)

Frankenstein (Graphic Revolve), Mary Shelley, retold by Michael Burgan (Raintree, 2009)

The Invisible Man (Graphic Chillers), H. G. Wells, retold by Joeming Dunn (Franklin Watts, 2010)

WEBSITE

learnenglishkids.britishcouncil.org/en/make-your-own/make-your-monster
Visit this website to create your own monster. You can also invent your own scary story, dangerous animal, or superhero.

Mighty Mighty MONSTERS

ADVENTURES

The King of Halloween Castle
ISBN: 978 1 406 23719 1

New Monster in School
ISBN: 978 1 406 23723 8

Monster Mansion
ISBN: 978 1 406 23721 4

My Missing Monster
ISBN: 978 1 406 23722 1

Lost in Spooky Forest
ISBN: 978 1 406 23720 7